rockschool®

Guitar Grade 8

*Performance pieces, technical exercises and in-depth guidance
for Rockschool examinations*

www.rockschool.co.uk

Acknowledgements

Published by Rockschool Ltd. © 2012
Catalogue Number RSK051209
ISBN: 978-1-908920-08-9
Revision 2 | 22 April 2013 | Errata details can be found at *www.rockschool.co.uk*

AUDIO
Recorded at Fisher Lane Studios
Produced and engineered by Nick Davis
Assistant engineer and Pro Tools operator Mark Binge
Mixed and mastered at Langlei Studios
Mixing and additional editing by Duncan Jordan
Supporting Tests recorded by Duncan Jordan and Kit Morgan
Mastered by Duncan Jordan
Executive producers: James Uings, Jeremy Ward and Noam Lederman

MUSICIANS
James Arben, Joe Bennett, Jason Bowld, Larry Carlton, Stuart Clayton, Andy Crompton, Neel Dhorajiwala, Fergus Gerrand, Charlie Griffiths, Felipe Karam, Kishon Khan, Noam Lederman, DJ Harry Love, Dave Marks, Kit Morgan, Jon Musgrave, Jake Painter, Richard Pardy, Ross Stanley, Stuart Ryan, Carl Sterling, Henry Thomas, Camilo Tirado, Simon Troup, James Uings, Steve Walker, Chris Webster, Norton York, Nir Z

PUBLISHING
Fact Files written by Joe Bennett, Charlie Griffiths, Stephen Lawson, Simon Pitt, Stuart Ryan and James Uings
Walkthroughs written by James Uings
Music engraving and book layout by Simon Troup and Jennie Troup of Digital Music Art
Proof reading and copy editing by Chris Bird, Claire Davies, Stephen Lawson, Simon Pitt and James Uings
Publishing administration by Caroline Uings
Cover design by Philip Millard

SYLLABUS
Syllabus director: Jeremy Ward
Instrumental specialists: Stuart Clayton, Noam Lederman and James Uings
Special thanks to: Brad Fuller and Georg Voros

SPONSORSHIP
Noam Lederman plays Mapex Drums, PAISTE cymbals and Vic Firth Sticks
Rockschool would like to thank the following companies for donating instruments used in the cover artwork

PRINTING
Printed and bound in the United Kingdom by Caligraving Ltd
CDs manufactured in the European Union by Software Logistics

DISTRIBUTION
Exclusive Distributors: Music Sales Ltd

CONTACTING ROCKSCHOOL
www.rockschool.co.uk
Telephone: +44 (0)845 460 4747
Fax: +44 (0)845 460 1960

Table of Contents

Introductions & Information

Rockschool Grade Pieces

Technical Exercises

Supporting Tests

Additional Information

Welcome to Rockschool Guitar Grade 8

Welcome to Guitar Grade 8

Welcome to the Rockschool Guitar Grade 8 pack. This book and CD contain everything you need to play guitar at this grade. In the book you will find the exam scores in both standard guitar notation and TAB. The CD has full stereo mixes of each tune, backing tracks to play along to for practice, and spoken two bar count-ins to both the full mixes and backing track versions of the songs.

Guitar Exams

At each grade, you have the option of taking one of two different types of examination:

- **Grade Exam:** a Grade Exam is a mixture of music performances, technical work and tests. You prepare three pieces (two of which may be Free Choice Pieces) and the contents of the Technical Exercise section. This accounts for 75% of the exam marks. The other 25% consists of: a Quick Study Piece (10%), a pair of instrument specific Ear Tests (10%), and finally you will be asked five General Musicianship Questions (5%). The pass mark is 60%.

- **Performance Certificate:** in a Performance Certificate you play five pieces. Up to three of these can be Free Choice Pieces. Each song is marked out of 20 and the pass mark is 60%.

Book Contents

The book is divided into a number of sections. These are:

- **Exam Pieces:** in this book you will find six specially commissioned pieces of Grade 8 standard. Each of these is preceded by a *Fact File*. Each Fact File contains a summary of the song, its style, tempo, key and technical features, along with a list of the musicians who played on it. There is additional information on the techniques and style as well as recommended further listening. The song is printed on up to four pages. Immediately after each song is a *Walkthrough*. This covers the song from a performance perspective, focusing on the technical issues you will encounter along the way. Each Walkthrough features two graphical musical 'highlights' showing particular parts of the song. Each song comes with a full mix version and a backing track. Both versions have spoken count-ins at the beginning. Please note that any solos played on the full mix versions are indicative only.

- **Technical Exercises:** you should prepare the exercises set in this grade in the keys indicated. You should also choose *one* Stylistic Study from the three printed to practise and play to the backing track in the exam. The style you choose will determine the style of the Quick Study Piece.

- **Supporting Tests and General Musicianship Questions:** in Guitar Grade 8 there are three supporting tests – a Quick Study Piece, a pair of Ear Tests and a set of General Musicianship Questions (GMQs) asked at the end of each exam. Examples of the types of tests likely to appear in the exam are printed in this book. Additional test examples of both types of test and the GMQs can be found in the Rockschool *Guitar Companion Guide*.

- **General Information:** finally, you will find information on exam procedures, including online examination entry, marking schemes, and what to do when arriving, and waiting, for your exam.

We hope you enjoy using this book. You will find a *Syllabus Guide* for Guitar and other exam information on our website: *www.rockschool.co.uk*. Rockschool Graded Music Exams are accredited in England, Wales and Northern Ireland by Ofqual, the DfE and CCEA and by SQA Accreditation in Scotland.

SONG TITLE: MEET DARTH EAR

GENRE: PROGRESSIVE METAL

TEMPO: 120 BPM

KEY: E MINOR

TECH FEATURES: ALTERNATE PICKING

SYNCOPATED RIFFS

TIME SIGNATURE CHANGES

COMPOSERS: CHARLIE GRIFFITHS
& JASON BOWLD

PERSONNEL: CHARLIE GRIFFITHS (GTR)
DAVE MARKS (BASS)
JASON BOWLD (DRUMS)

OVERVIEW

'Meet Darth Ear' is a progressive metal track in the style of bands like Dream Theater, Periphery and Symphony X. It begins with an alternate picked 16th note riff followed by a crunchy E phrygian section that features numerous odd time changes. The melodic verse uses extended arpeggios based in E natural minor. This is a challenging section to play cleanly because there are lots of string changes and position shifts. The chorus comprises of ringing sustained chords that provide some respite before the solo, which is played over a similar natural minor based progression to that of the verse.

STYLE FOCUS

Progressive metal features heavy, technical riffs that are usually played with a tone and intensity comparable to those of thrash metal but with more complex rhythms and lots of time signature changes. The style demands technical excellence and precision in all metal based techniques but relies mainly on alternate picking and legato. Prog metal compositions are often long and contain various dynamic shifts. It's common for lead guitar parts to switch between modes: lydian, phrygian, harmonic minor and melodic minor are the most frequently used.

THE BIGGER PICTURE

Prog metal emerged in the late 1980s when Queensrÿche, Fates Warning and other metal bands were influenced by the cerebral approach of 1970s prog rock bands like Yes, Rush and King Crimson. In 1992, a group of ex-Berklee College of Music students named Dream Theater refined this concept and released *Images And Words* (1992), an album with a level of musicianship never heard before in metal. John Petrucci displayed guitar chops to match the likes of Steve Vai, while the complex song structures and highly arranged unison passages were unrivalled. Today Dream Theater continue to dominate the genre. However, bands like Tool, Porcupine Tree and Opeth have diversified the sound considerably.

RECOMMENDED LISTENING

Queensrÿche's conceptual masterpiece *Operation: Mindcrime* (1988) is a must. Its cinematic feel and Chris DeGarmo's imaginative guitar parts were a big influence on prog metal pioneers Fates Warning, who hit their stride in 1991 with their breakthrough album *Parallels*. Dream Theater released the masterpiece *Images And Words* a year later and *Awake* in 1994. More recently, Pain of Salvation's album *Remedy Lane* (2002) has become a modern classic.

Meet Darth Ear

Charlie Griffiths & Jason Bowld

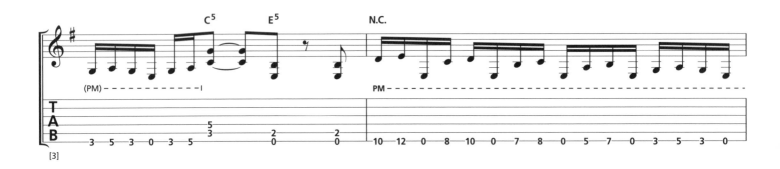

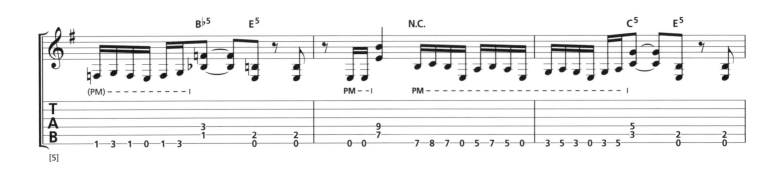

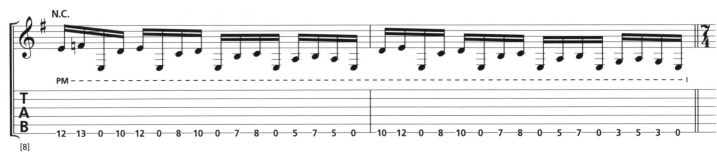

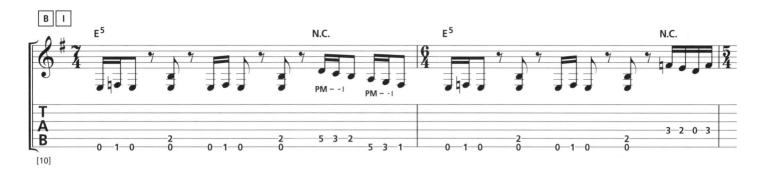

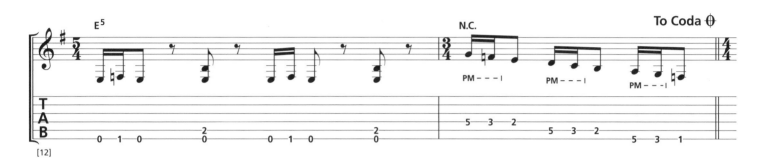

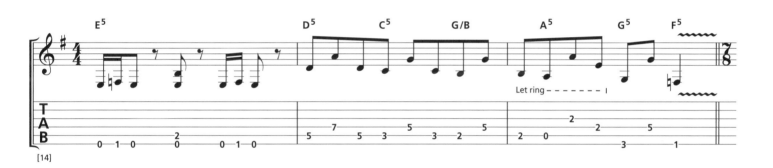

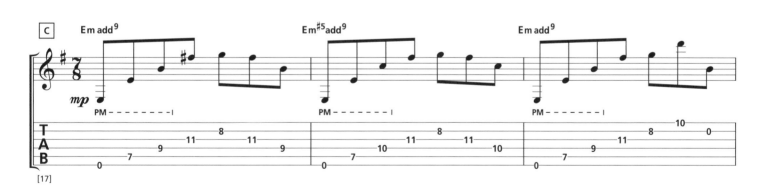

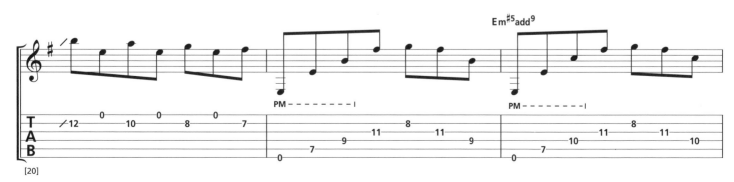

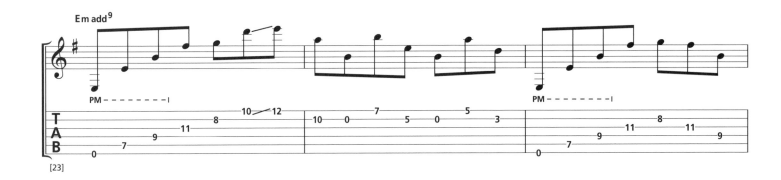

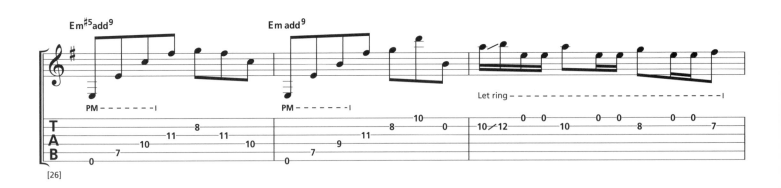

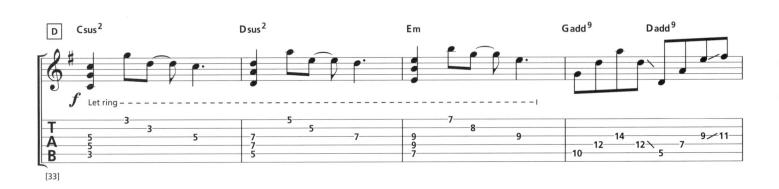

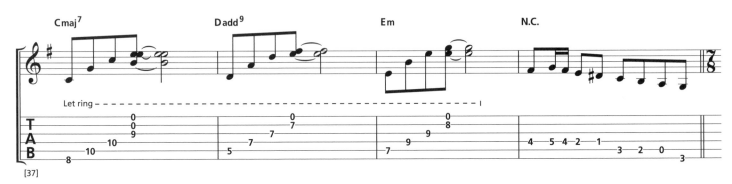

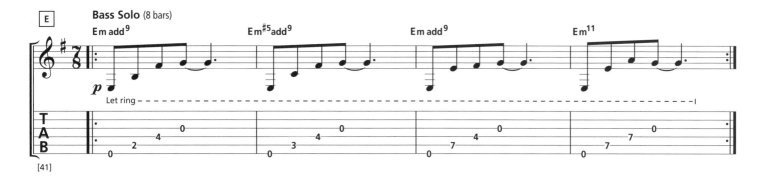

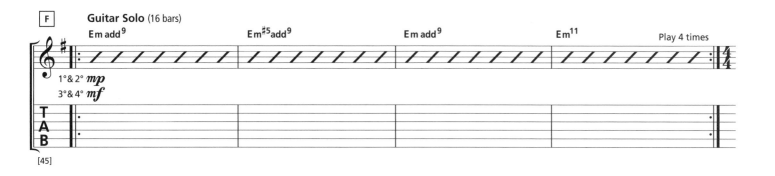

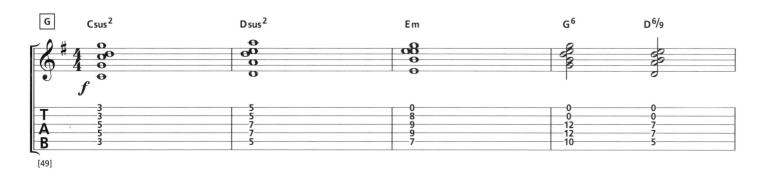

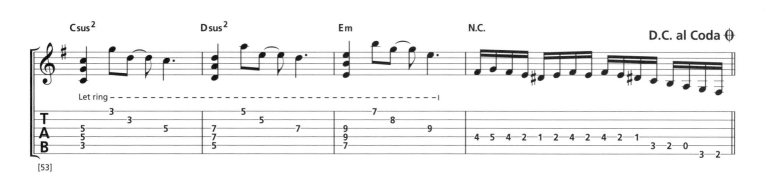

Coda

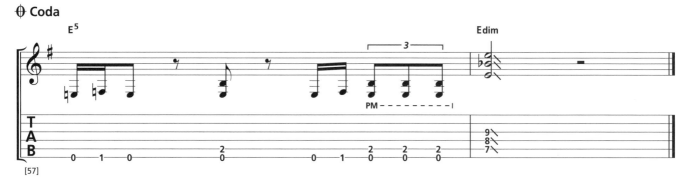

Walkthrough

Amp Settings

The traditional scooped metal tone will work for most of 'Meet Darth Ear' but you may wish to switch to a sound with more middle for the solo. Metal rhythm tones are usually dry (without effects), but it's common to add delay in more melodic sections and solos.

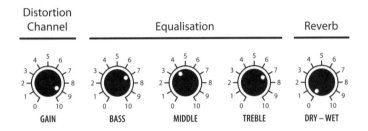

A & H Sections (Bars 1–9)

This section consists of a heavy riff that combines powerchords with low string palm-muted single-note runs that use the E string as a pedal tone.

Bars 1–9 | *Fast picking*
Many of the riffs in 'Meet Darth Ear' feature fast alternate picking, often with palm muting, and will probably take some preparation to play well. Use a relaxed picking action and minimise excess motion where possible: your pick should only travel a small amount past the string. Work on these phrases with the metronome set to a lower speed and only increase it when you can play the part accurately.

B & I Sections (Bars 10–16)

This section is a variation of the opening riff that uses different time signatures.

Bars 10–13 | *Odd time signatures*
If you look closely at these bars you will see that they are based on a five beat riff (Fig. 1). The 7/4 bar is this riff followed by a two-beat phrase. The 6/4 bar is this pattern followed by a one-beat phrase and bar 12 is the five-beat riff on its own followed by a three-beat phrase in bar 13.

C Section (Bars 17–32)

In the C section, the time signature changes to 7/8 and the guitar arpeggiates exotic sounding chords.

Bars 17–31 | *7/8 time signature*
The 7/8 time signature is usually counted as a group of four beats followed by a group of three beats ("1 2 3 4 1 2 3"). If you count along with the music as you are playing, you will find that this time signature has a unique groove which you should be able to lock into and feel naturally.

D & E Sections (Bars 33–44)

The D section is a melodic part that uses chords such as the sus^2 and add^9 to create an open sound. The E section is the bass solo where the time signature returns to 7/8.

Bars 33–44 | *Combining fretted notes with open strings*
Take time to ensure that you play the fretted notes with the tips of your fingers so that the open strings can ring freely.

F & G Sections (Bars 45–56)

The F section is the guitar solo and changes dynamic halfway through. The F section is a frenetic drum solo. Although the guitar plays a simple part, full concentration will be required to maintain the pulse.

Bars 45–48 | *Guitar solo*
The biggest challenge of this solo is playing convincingly in 7/8 time. Start by counting through the bar ("1 2 3 4 1 2 3") playing a note on every beat (Fig. 2). Accent the first beat of each bar to help you feel where the start of each bar is. Once you feel comfortable, play phrases that are more rhythmically interesting but maintain the accent on beat one to remind you of the groove. Once you feel you are improvising fluently you should find that you do not have to keep the beat one accent.

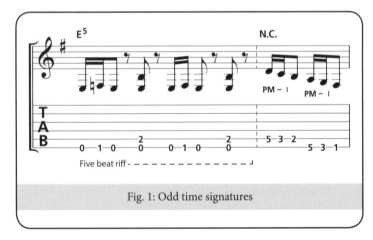

Fig. 1: Odd time signatures

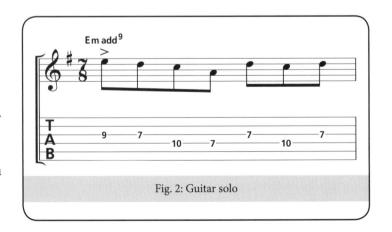

Fig. 2: Guitar solo

SONG TITLE: MIND THE GAPS

GENRE: FUNK

TEMPO: 96 BPM

KEY: B♭

TECH FEATURES: MUTED 16ᵀᴴ NOTE RHYTHMS
ALTERED CHORDS

COMPOSER: KIT MORGAN

PERSONNEL: LARRY CARLTON (GTR)
HENRY THOMAS (BASS)
NOAM LEDERMAN (DRUMS)
FERGUS GERRAND (PERC)
ROSS STANLEY (KEYS)
FULL FAT HORNS (BRASS)

OVERVIEW

'Mind The Gaps' is a funk track in the style of Average White Band, The Crusaders and Tower Of Power. It features triads, altered chords – and a special guest appearance by fusion legend Larry Carlton.

STYLE FOCUS

This piece will test your ability to hold down a tight funk chord part and solo over a complex chord progression. In this type of instrumental funk track the guitar is often at the fore playing melody lines and using more sophisticated and unusual chord voicings. There are also situations where the guitar is the only instrument playing chords so an advanced chord vocabulary is essential, especially if you are to create an interesting harmonic backdrop for a soloist.

THE BIGGER PICTURE

In the 1970s, black music styles merged as jazz musicians achieved commercial success via the popular rhythmic appeal of funk and soul. Groups like Tower Of Power, The Crusaders and Average White Band were able to draw on their knowledge of jazz harmony to create a more complex form of funky soul music that didn't rely as heavily on one-chord vamps as much as James Brown's funk did.

There were those, however, who admired funk's rough edges as much as its rhythmic pull. Miles Davis and Herbie Hancock were established on the jazz scene when Brown created funk in the late 1960s. Both were seduced by its earthiness and wondered how their own improvised music might sound with a stable harmonic base, the complex chords and quick changes of bebop discarded completely. Davis' *Bitches Brew* (1970) and Hancock's *Headhunters* (1973) provided the answer; two wild jazz funk albums of a different nature to their slick contemporaries.

Donald Byrd and his protégés The Blackbyrds occupied the middle ground. The Blackbyrds' eponymous debut (1974) swung from heavy James Brown style funk grooves to jazzy soul improvisations.

RECOMMENDED LISTENING

Tower Of Power's eponymous release of 1973 features their funkiest track, 'What Is Hip?', while Average White Band's 'Pick Up The Pieces' has instrumental funk chord voicings and a catchy rhythm part. Finally, for smooth jazz listen to 'Room 335' from Larry Carlton's self-titled 1978 album.

Mind The Gaps

Tracks 3 & 4

Kit Morgan

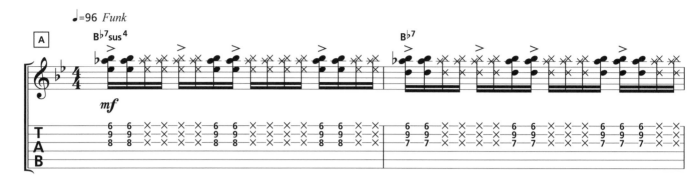

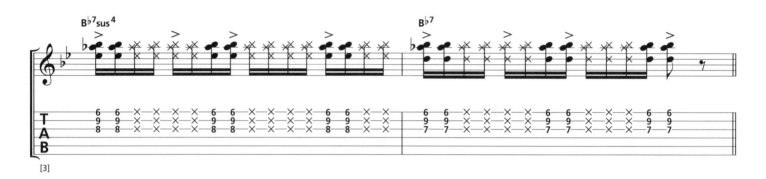

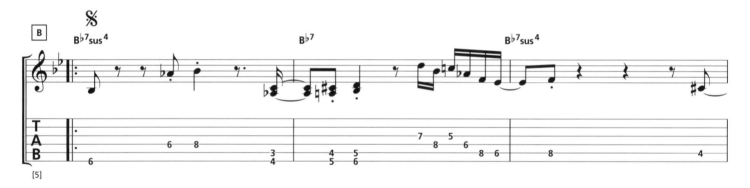

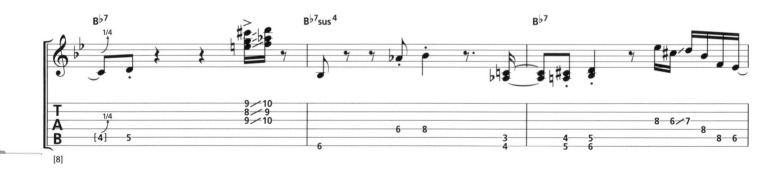

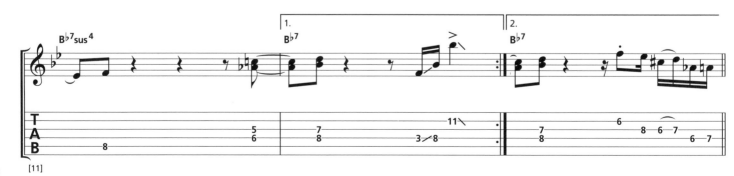

Guitar Grade 8

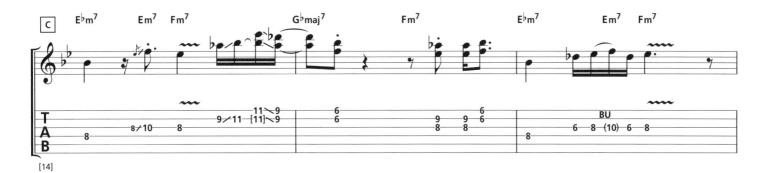

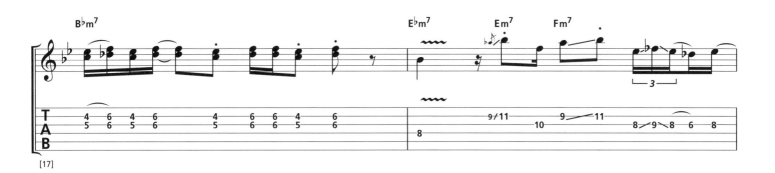

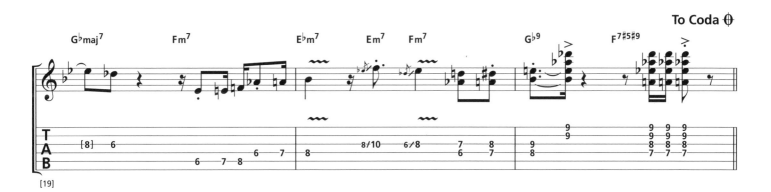

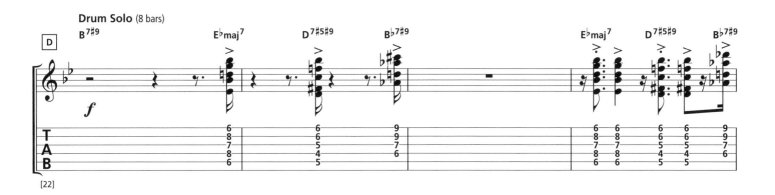

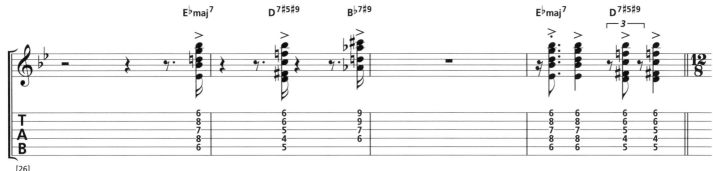

E   **Guitar Solo** (16 bars)

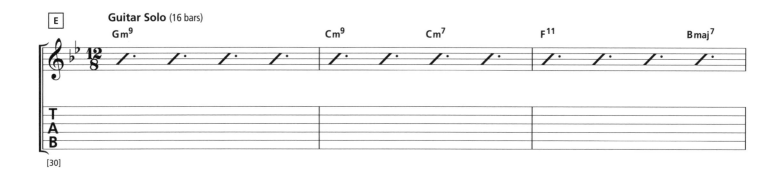

[30]

[33]

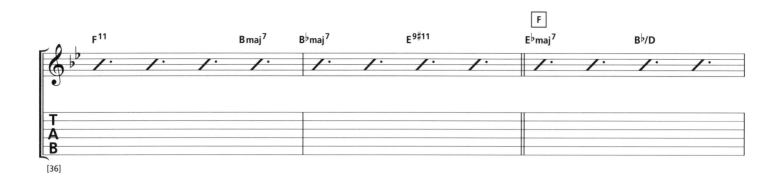

[36]

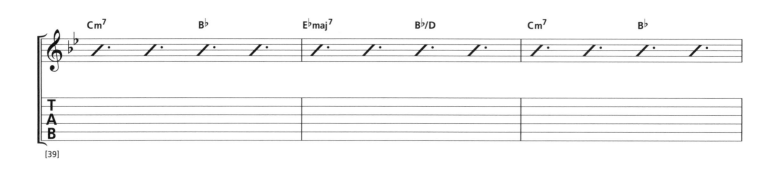

[39]

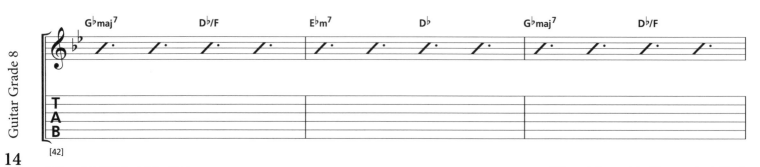

[42]

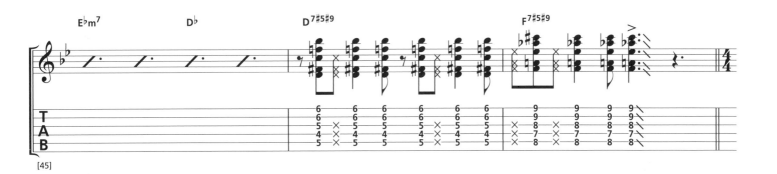

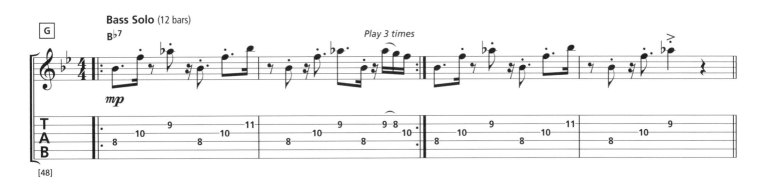

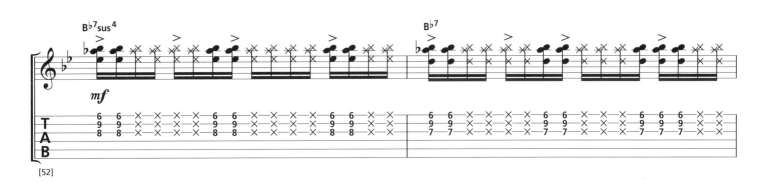

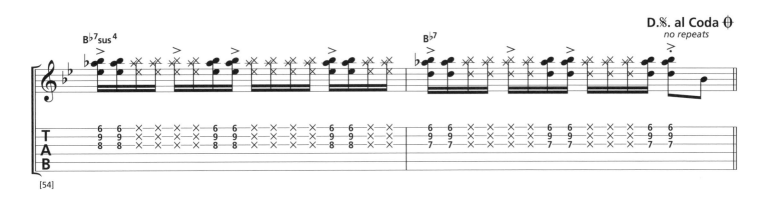

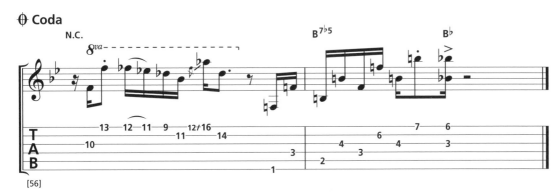

Guitar Grade 8

Walkthrough

Amp Settings

A slightly overdriven tone is used on the recording but you can also use a clean tone for the majority of the song and switch to a distorted tone for the guitar solo. Aim for a light overdrive and make sure you retain clarity.

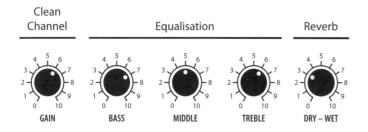

A section (Bars 1–4)

The A section is an accented 16th-note rhythm that uses a combination of three-note chords and muted strings.

Bars 1–4 | Accents
The accents in bars 1–4 are trickier to articulate than they may first appear, and the main challenge is to play an accent while your fingers are not holding a chord.

B Section (Bars 5–13)

The B section is a funky, syncopated melody that combines single-note lines with double-stops and chords.

Bars 5–13 | Playing tightly
When playing mid-tempo funk tracks guitarists often rush ahead of the beat, especially when there are big gaps between phrases. Relax and aim to really lock in to the groove.

C Section (Bars 14–21)

This syncopated melody uses a range of articulations like staccato notes, double-stop slides and hammer-ons.

Bar 17 | Double-stop hammer-on
Fret the E♭ and C notes with your first and second fingers and then hammer-on with the pad of your third finger so that you fret both the B and G strings. Listen closely to ensure both notes ring out because it's easy to miss the B string as you hammer-on (Fig. 1).

D Section (Bars 22–29)

The drum solo is accompanied by heavily syncopated stabs that use extended chords such as the 7♯9 and 7♯5♯9.

Bars 22–29 | Syncopated stabs
Avoid rushing accented notes and chords at slow tempos with large rests by using a metronome. Count through the bars, aiming to place each note *exactly* on the correct beat.

E & F Sections (Bars 30–47)

In the E and F sections the song changes to the 12/8 time signature for the guitar solo. The E section is in G minor whereas the F section moves into more modal territory.

Bars 30–45 | Scale choices
The first half of the solo is based in G minor and the natural minor will work through the majority of it. The second half is based on the same set of notes but outlines E♭ lydian before the progression modulates to G♭ lydian (they can also be considered as 'standard' major progressions). While the change from G minor to E♭ lydian simply requires a shift of the tonal centre, practise the modulation from E♭ to G♭ otherwise the change in scale may sound unmusical.

G Section (Bars 48–55)

This heavily syncopated single-note line accompanies the bass solo before returning to the groove in the A section.

Bars 48–51 | Complex rhythms
You may find this riff easier to learn by ear. Listen closely to the recording for the rhythm. Alternatively, count through the bar in 16th notes (see example in Fig. 2) and work out where in the bar each note falls and practise slowly.

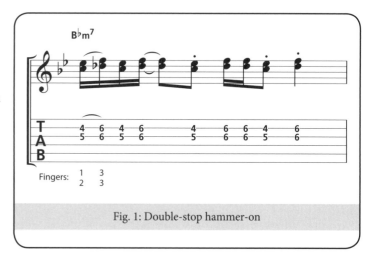

Fig. 1: Double-stop hammer-on

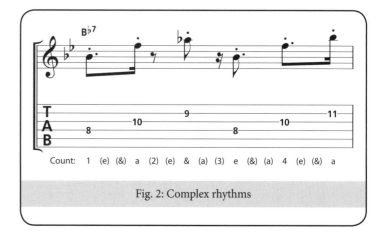

Fig. 2: Complex rhythms

SONG TITLE: LEAD SHEET

GENRE: ROCK

TEMPO: 98 BPM

KEY: F♯ MINOR

TECH FEATURES: OCTAVES

16TH NOTE TRIPLETS

TWO HANDED TAPPING

COMPOSER: JAMES UINGS

PERSONNEL: STUART RYAN (GTR)

DAVE MARKS (BASS)

NOAM LEDERMAN (DRUMS)

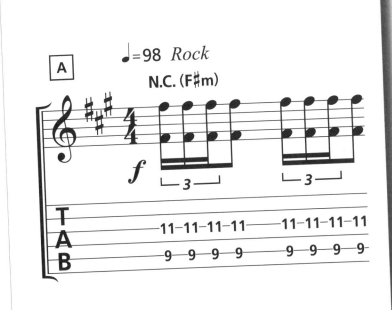

OVERVIEW

'Lead Sheet' is a rap rock track in the style of Rage Against The Machine (RATM), Limp Bizkit and Red Hot Chili Peppers (RHCP). It features octaves, 16th note triplets and two-hand tapping.

STYLE FOCUS

Rap rock bands are influenced by the production of hip hop tracks where producers sample short sections of songs then loop them. As a result, rap rock riffs tend to be small, self-contained cells repeated throughout verse and/or chorus sections. Most of these riffs are based on the minor pentatonic or blues scales. 'Lead Sheet' is set in F♯ minor and therefore follows a tradition that runs from Led Zeppelin's 'Immigrant Song' to RATM's 'Bombtrack'. Rage guitarist Tom Morello developed a unique style that mimicked a DJ's turntable techniques and was an influence on later bands like Korn and Limp Bizkit.

THE BIGGER PICTURE

Hip hop producers have been sampling rock riffs since the mid 1980s when Run DMC, Public Enemy, and Beastie Boys all scored hits that borrowed from

Aerosmith, Slayer and Led Zeppelin. RHCP and RATM saw the potential in this rock rap crossover and combined distorted guitar riffs with rap vocals.

RHCP's album *BloodSugarSexMagik* (1991) spawned the rap rock classics 'Funky Monks', 'Suck My Kiss' and 'Sir Psycho Sexy'. The following year, RATM released their self-titled debut and turned a generation of rockers on to a form of rock where groove and aggression were key.

This next wave of rap rockers included Limp Bizkit and Incubus. Unlike RATM, whose guitarist Tom Morello simulated turntable effects, these groups employed DJs to introduce hip hop techniques including scratching and cutting.

RECOMMENDED LISTENING

RCHP's *BloodSugarSexMagik* is the most rap orientated of their albums. RATM's debut is essential listening, particularly the songs 'Bombtrack', 'Bullet In The Head' and 'Know Your Enemy'. 'Bulls On Parade', from their 1996 follow-up *Evil Empire*, is also recommended. Limp Bizkit's *Chocolate Starfish And The Hotdog Flavoured Water* (2000) is worth investigating for 'My Generation', 'Rollin'' and 'Take A Look Around'.

Lead Sheet

James Uings

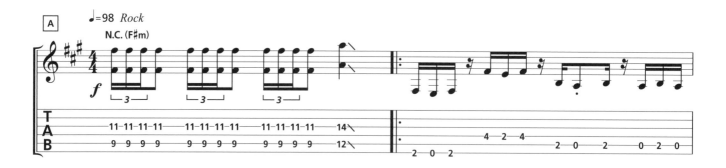

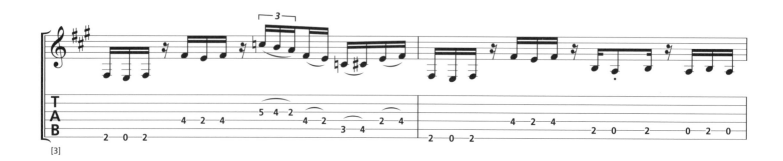

[3]

[5]

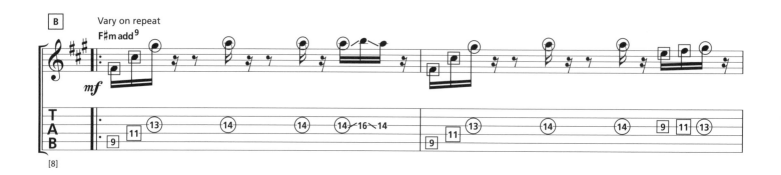

[8]

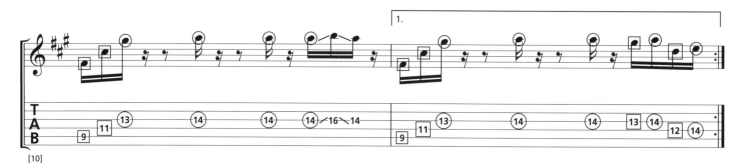

[10]

18

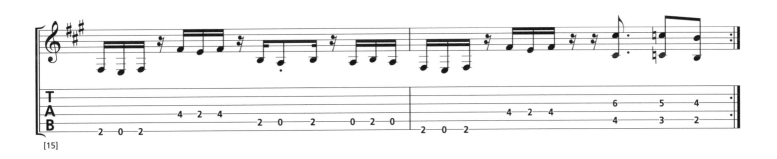

E | **Guitar Solo** (12 bars)

F#m

Play 3 times

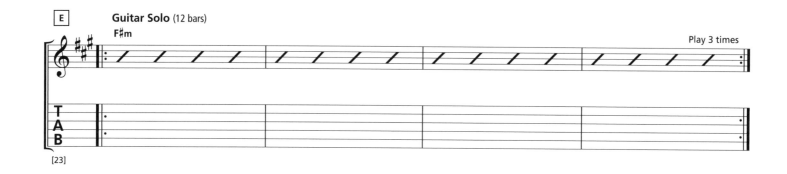

[23]

Drum Solo (12 bars)

F

Grad. cresc.

F#5   A5

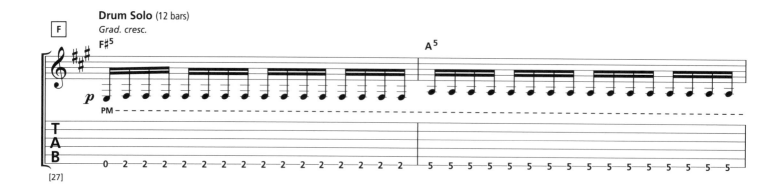

[27]

B5   C#5   D5   E5

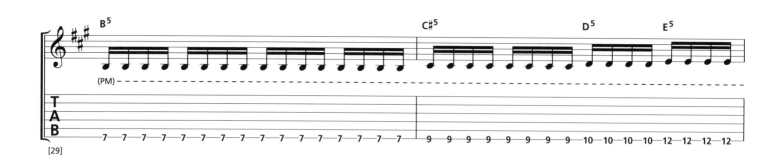

[29]

F#5   A5

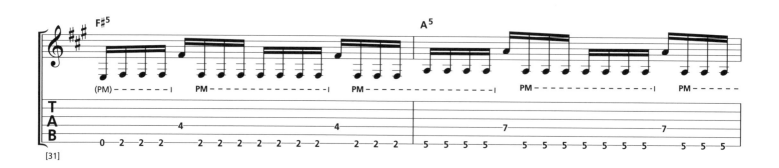

[31]

B5   C#5   D5   E5

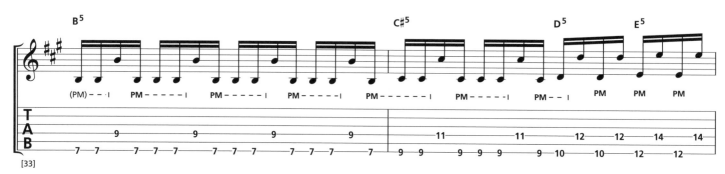

[33]

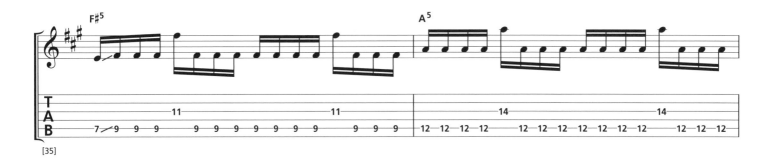

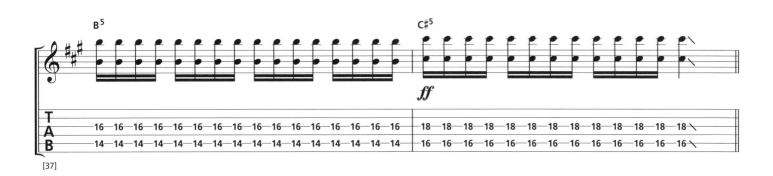

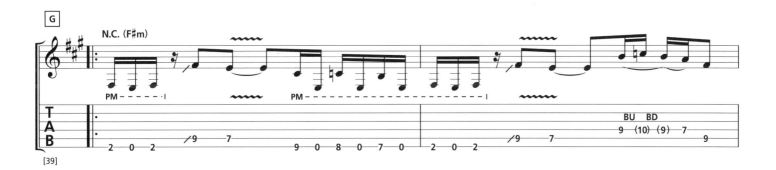

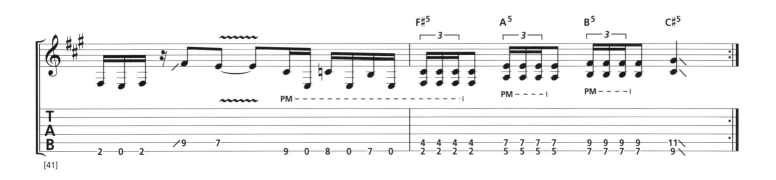

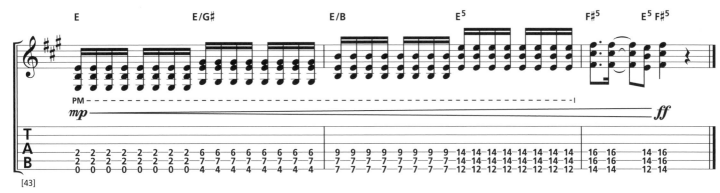

Walkthrough

Amp Settings

Use a modern high-gain distortion but set the gain a little lower than you would on most other kinds of rock and metal. You may wish to add some delay in the tapped sections and boost the gain for the guitar solo.

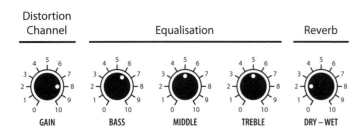

A Section (Bars 1–7)

The A section starts with octaves played in unison with the bass and drums before moving to a syncopated single-note riff based on the blues scale.

Bar 1 | *Sixteenth-note triplets*

The fast octaves to be found in this bar are best played with a down up down up strumming action for each set of four notes. This means that the final eighth note will then be played using an upstroke, which may feel uncomfortable at first (Fig. 1).

Bar 3 | *Legato phrasing*

The first three notes of beat three are undoubtedly the most challenging of this phrase. The two pull-offs should be executed as one smooth movement by snapping your fretting hand towards the floor. Even though it is one overall motion, make sure both pull-offs sound cleanly as it is common for the second note to be lost in this kind of lick.

B & C Sections (Bars 8–18)

The A section uses two-handed tapping to outline the chords and play a melody line. The C section is a reprise of the A section.

Bars 8–13 | *Two-handed tapping*

The first two notes of each bar are played by hammering your fretting fingers onto the fretboard without picking (marked with a square). Hammer down firmly to make a clean contact and avoid unwanted string noise. Notes that are circled are tapped with the picking hand. This riff will take a while to co-ordinate so start slowly and gradually build up speed.

D & E Sections (Bars 19–26)

The D section is the bass solo where the guitar plays stabs with the drums. The E section is the guitar solo.

Bars 23–26 | *Guitar solo*

This 12-bar solo is played over a repeated blues scale riff played by the bass. With a solo of this length over a riff that implies a single chord, it is easy to fall into playing collections of licks rather than creating a coherent musical idea. You will need to plan out a basic structure (even if you improvise within this) to build an effective solo that has direction and complements the song.

F & G Sections (Bars 27–45)

The F section is the drum solo, over which the guitar plays a part that builds in volume and intensity. The G section is a riff that uses heavy palm muting, 16th note triplets, and climaxes with a gradual build using three-note chords moving through different inversions of the E chord.

Bar 34 | *Fast octave picking*

This bar features some fast string skipping. Strict alternate picking is undoubtedly the way to play this phrase (Fig. 2). You should also work to minimise the motion in your picking action to play this challenging phrase up to speed.

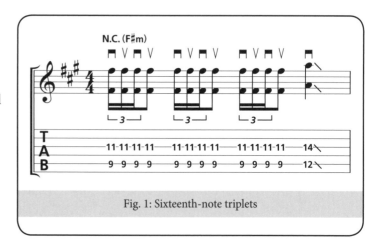

Fig. 1: Sixteenth-note triplets

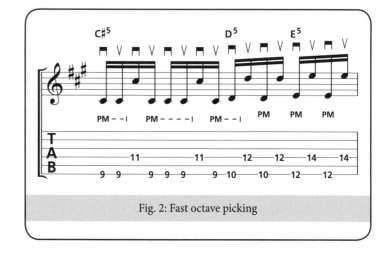

Fig. 2: Fast octave picking

SONG TITLE: FREIGHTSHAKER

GENRE: BLUES

TEMPO: 160 BPM

KEY: A MINOR (BLUES)

TECH FEATURES: FAST TRIPLET LICKS

9TH CHORDS

ARPEGGIATED CHORDS

COMPOSER: SIMON TROUP

PERSONNEL: STUART RYAN (GTR)

HENRY THOMAS (BASS)

NOAM LEDERMAN (DRUMS)

ROSS STANLEY (KEYS)

OVERVIEW

'Freightshaker' is an uptempo blues composition with a strong Texan influence à la Stevie Ray Vaughan, Kenny Wayne Sheppard and Walter Trout. It features fast triplet licks, sophisticated accompaniment chords, and heavily swung riffing among its techniques.

STYLE FOCUS

Fast Texan blues is exciting and poses some technical challenges for you to enjoy. In the trio format, timing, touch and tone have to be spot on: if you lose your place it can be difficult to get back onboard. Dynamics are also critical when playing within the trio format. Here, for example, knowing when to dig in and when to sit back is the difference between a good and a great performance. As a rule, sitting back while the other instruments solo and digging in harder for your own solo works well. This style of blues requires a heavier guitar tone and a strong pick attack, as demonstrated by Vaughan.

THE BIGGER PICTURE

Although he was by no means the first, Vaughan is considered the greatest of the Texan bluesmen. He rose to fame after he and his band Double Trouble were discovered by Jackson Browne and David Bowie at the Montreaux Jazz Festival of 1982. Influenced a great deal by Jimi Hendrix, Vaughan's knowledge of the blues was encyclopedic and his technique was more adept than even his hero's.

After supplying the Albert King style licks for Bowie's *Let's Dance*, Vaughan was offered the lead guitar slot in a two year tour with Bowie but turned it down to prioritise his own band. Their 1983 debut, *Texas Flood*, should be a cornerstone of any self-respecting blues fan's record collection.

Vaughan died in a helicopter accident in August 1990, but his playing still inspires young blues players like Kenny Wayne Sheppard and Philip Sayce.

RECOMMENDED LISTENING

To hear the uptempo side of blues, take a listen to Vaughan's 'Testify' or 'Scuttle Buttin'. Joe Bonamassa also plays with great technique and control at higher speeds as displayed on tracks like 'Travellin' South' from his 2004 album *Had To Cry Today*. Blues rock legend Gary Moore was especially adept at high speed blues riffing and soloing, as heard on *Blues Alive* (1993) and the guitar solo on 'Walking By Myself.'

Freightshaker

Simon Troup

Walkthrough

Amp Settings

Opt for an aggressive, overdriven tone with plenty of bite. Set the gain quite high and boost the middle to help the guitar's sound cut through the mix, particularly during the solo. You can either switch to a clean tone for the quieter sections or simply turn your guitar's volume control down to produce a less distorted tone.

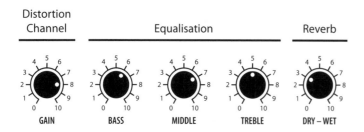

A Section (Bars 1–4)

The A section consists of double-stops played in a syncopated rhythm with heavy vibrato.

Bars 1–4 | *Double-stop vibrato*

Barre the B and G strings with the pad of your first finger and apply vibrato as you play the notated rhythm. Make sure movement is even and consistent and that both strings ring out throughout the phrase.

B & C sections (Bars 5–36)

The B and C sections are bluesy riffs that use single notes, double-stops and staccato 9th chords.

Bar 8 | *Trill*

Trills are indicated by the sign above the notation (Fig. 1). When you see this you should rapidly alternate between the two notes shown in brackets. In this case, the trill is articulated with hammer-ons and pull-offs on the G string while the D string rings alongside the trill.

Bars 23 | *Double-stop legato lick*

Barre your first finger across the E, B and G strings at the fifth fret and play the D on the G string with your third finger. Play the G string with your pick and use one of your picking hand fingers to pluck the E string. Perform the fast legato run with your third and fourth fingers. The final note is played using the still-barred first finger, and the E string should ring out until beat two.

Bars 31–32 | *Fast triplet run*

Play this high speed phrase using alternate picking (Fig. 2). Use a relaxed picking action and minimise excess motion – your pick should only travel a small amount past the string. Work on these phrases with the metronome set to a lower speed and only increase it when you can play accurately.

D Section (Bars 37–60)

The D section is a 16-bar guitar solo in the key of A. Your main challenge will be creating a solo that is convincing stylistically and suitable for the grade.

Bars 37–60 | *Guitar solo*

Blues is generally predisposed to blues scale and minor pentatonic licks, so the A minor pentatonic and blues scales will work here. However, at this grade you may wish to explore more advanced ideas. One option is to use the relevant mixolydian mode over each dominant 7 chord. However, another option is to base your ideas on dominant 7th or 9th arpeggios.

E, F & G Sections (61–104)

The E section starts with arpeggiated extended chords before moving to choppy rhythms. The F section features the drum solo and the B section is repeated, giving you the opportunity to vary the part. The G section contains the bass solo where you can create your own accompaniment.

Bars 85–96 | *Accompanying a solo*

This is where you compose an accompaniment for the bass solo. While you must craft an interesting part, remember that your primary goal is to support the soloist.

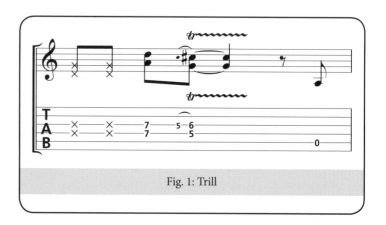

Fig. 1: Trill

Fig. 2: Fast triplet run

SONG TITLE: NOSSO SAMBA

GENRE: SAMBA

TEMPO: 110 BPM

KEY: G MAJOR

TECH FEATURES: FINGERPICKED CHORDS

16TH NOTE STRUMMING

COMPOSER: NOAM LEDERMAN

PERSONNEL: NOAM LEDERMAN (DRUMS)

HENRY THOMAS (BASS)

STUART RYAN (GTR)

KISHON KHAN (KEYS)

FERGUS GERRAND (PERC)

CHRIS WEBSTER (TROMBONE)

OVERVIEW

'Nosso Samba' is written in the style of classic Brazilian artists such as the revered Antonio Carlos Jobim and Gilberto Gil, and the modern day samba group Nosso Trio. It features octave melodies, fingerpicked chords and 16th note strumming patterns among its techniques.

STYLE FOCUS

Since the bossa nova era of the 1950s, samba has had much in common with jazz. A lot of the music is improvised so a familiarity with playing over standards and changes will be of benefit to a student of the Brazilian music 'Nosso Samba' is based on. The bossa nova rhythm style is usually played with thumb and fingers, although you could achieve the same effect using a combination of pick and fingers.

THE BIGGER PICTURE

Samba is the rhythmic, syncopated music of Brazil with its roots in the African culture of the country's black population. The first samba record is believed to be a song called 'Pelo Telefono' that was released in 1917, and gave the style its first significant exposure

outside of the favelas (slums). Early samba relied on the power of drums and percussion, and was revered for its raw energy rather than musical sophistication.

However, this changed in the 1950s when young middle class suburbanites like João Gilberto and Jobim brought in supple melodies and jazz influenced harmonies. This new style, or 'bossa nova', exposed Brazilian music to the world; its best known song is 'The Girl From Ipanema', which was translated into English and performed by Frank Sinatra.

More recently, Nosso Trio have developed modern samba and inspired instrumentalists from every corner of the planet to explore Brazilian music. The trio's guitarist, Nelson Faria, attended Los Angeles' Guitar Institute Of Technology where he studied under fusion guitarists Scott Henderson and Frank Gambale. He has since written books and produced videos about Brazilian guitar playing.

RECOMMENDED LISTENING

Gilberto's *Chega De Saudade* (1959) is a bossa nova classic. To hear how Brazilian music changed in the 1960s, listen to *Caetano Veloso* (1968) by Caetano Veloso. Finally, Nosso Trio's modern take on samba can be heard on their 2006 debut *Vento Bravo*.

Nosso Samba

Noam Lederman

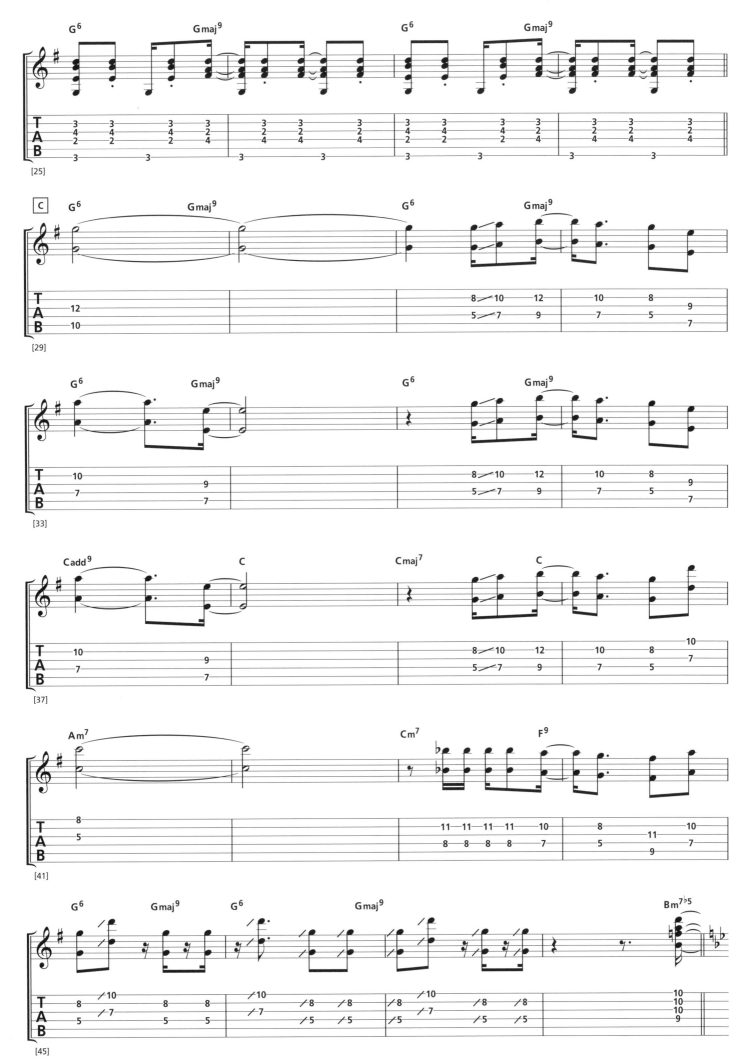

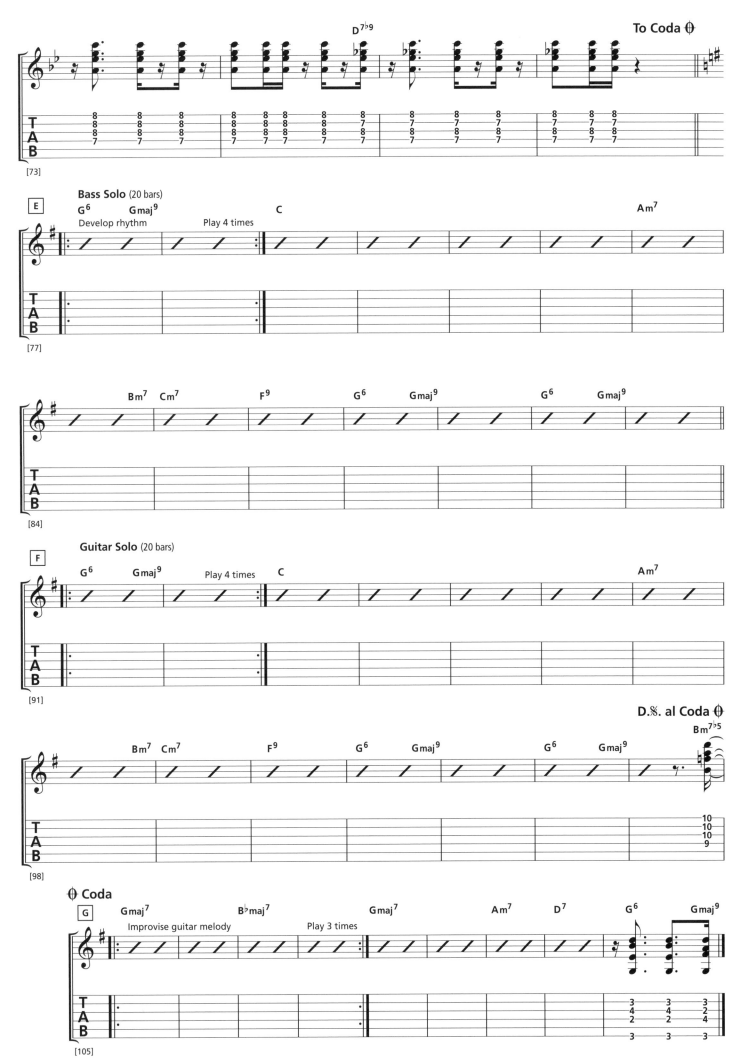

Walkthrough

Amp Settings
Aim for a clean tone that's full and warm. Using your guitar's neck pickup will help with this. Boost the bass (but don't let the sound become too muddy) and roll off the middle and treble if you feel the sound is too harsh. Reverb, if available, will greatly enhance the mood of this piece.

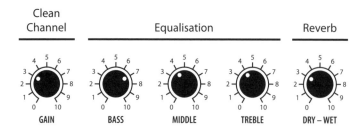

A & B sections (Bars 1–28)
The A & B sections are based on a fingerpicked chordal groove. The A section is a drum solo while the B section involves the bass playing the melody.

Bars 10–11 | *Cuíca*
The A section ends with an imitation of a cuíca, which is a high pitched sounding Brazilian drum. This unique sound is achieved by quickly sliding up from several frets below each note. This quick movement is challenging and you should ensure that the destination notes are played in time.

C Section (Bars 29–48)
The C section consists of an octave melody. Syncopated rhythms and fast position shifts make this a tricky section.

Bars 29–47 | *Sliding octaves*
Approach slides octaves in the same way as playing powerchords and barre chords: lock your fingers in position and move the fretting hand as a unit rather than dealing with individual finger placement.

D Section (Bars 49–76)
This intense rhythmic part uses, among others, several altered chords played on the first four strings of the guitar

Bars 49–76 | *Complex rhythms*
This rhythm will take some preparation to master. Work slowly while counting 16th notes ("1 e & a 2 e & a 3 e & a 4 e & a") (Fig. 1). Aim to 'feel' the rhythm rather than counting it to help your performance sound more convincing. A 16th note strumming pattern will help keep the pulse throughout the numerous syncopated rhythms.

E & F Sections (Bars 77–104)
The E section is the bass solo. The F section is a guitar solo.

Bars 77–90 | *Accompanying a solo*
While you must create an interesting part to accompany the bass solo, your primary goal is to support the soloist.

Bars 91–104 | *Guitar solo*
The G major scale will work throughout bars 91–98 and the C dorian mode for bars 99–100. Many jazz players opt for the lydian mode over the major scale because its ♯4 interval introduces tension that the major scale does not provide. If you wish to try this approach use G lydian in bars 91–92 and C lydian in bars 93–98.

G Section (Bars 105–113)
The G section is another opportunity for you to create you own part. This time, improvise a melody that complements the two-hand tapped part the bassist is playing.

Bars 105–113 | *G maj 7 – B♭ maj 7 chord change*
Rather than changing scale position every time the chord changes (which may sound disjointed), stay in the same position and adjust the relevant notes every two bars. Start in G major then adjust the F♯, B and E to F♮, B♭ and E♭ respectively (Fig. 2).

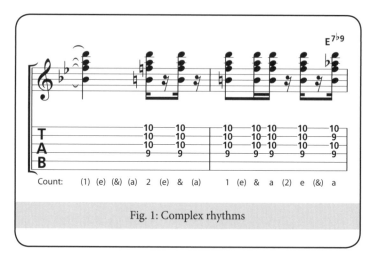

Fig. 1: Complex rhythms

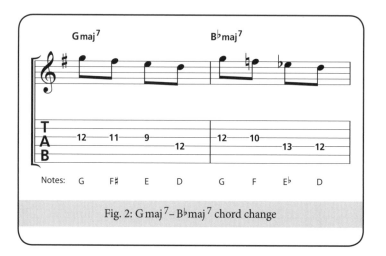

Fig. 2: G maj 7 – B♭ maj 7 chord change

SONG TITLE: DARK MATTER
GENRE: JAZZ
TEMPO: 121 BPM
KEY: A MINOR

TECH FEATURES: CHROMATICISM
FAST ALTERNATE PICKING
FUNK GROOVES

COMPOSERS: STUART RYAN, HENRY THOMAS
& KUNG FU DRUMMER

PERSONNEL: STUART RYAN (GTR)
HENRY THOMAS (BASS)
NOAM LEDERMAN (DRUMS)
JAMES ARBURN (SAX)

OVERVIEW

'Dark Matter' is a jazz funk piece in the style of Mike Stern and John Scofield. It features some challenging harmony interspersed with tight funk grooves. The melody is played as single notes, then with a darker sounding harmony. In keeping with this style there are chromatic ideas and displaced 16th note rhythms that require precise execution.

STYLE FOCUS

Jazz funk takes the harmony of jazz and combines it with the tight grooves of funk. Often a one-chord vamp will be used that allows the soloist to explore more complex scales and chromatic ideas. The chromatic runs in this piece offer a challenge to the picking hand and must be performed in time and with equal clarity to each note. In addition, this piece will test your timing and groove because you need to be able to play notes that are slightly displaced (i.e. not on the beat or offbeat but in between).

THE BIGGER PICTURE

Mike Stern and John Scofield came to prominence after performing with the legendary jazz trumpeter

and pioneer of fusion Miles Davis. Both Stern and Scofield have a sophisticated grasp of jazz harmony and are able to employ dissonance in their music that often leads to a sense of tension and release.

Unlike traditional bebop guitarists, Stern and Scofield incorporated tones and ideas drawn from rock and funk to make their writing unpredictable. Chromaticism (using notes that don't necessarily belong in the given key) is widespread in their playing. This type of guitarist has great technical command of his instrument and is equally at home playing blistering lead lines or accompanying with sophisticated jazz-based chords.

RECOMMENDED LISTENING

Stern's 1988 album *Time In Place* showcases his great technique and the chromatic approach to writing that informs many of his melody lines. Scofield's *Groove Elation* (1995) is an accessible album that also boasts Hammond organ and brass in the line-up. *Still Warm* (1985) also takes the complex writing and harmony typical of his style. Another noteworthy jazz funk guitarist was the late Hiram Bullock. Similar to Prince's music of the early 1990s, Bullock's 1992 album *Way Kool* incorporated rhythms from the new jack swing genre popular at the time.

Dark Matter

Stuart Ryan, Henry Thomas & Kung Fu Drummer

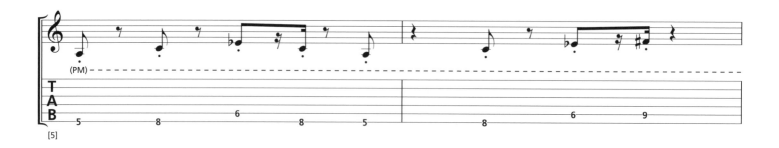

[11]

[13]

Fine

[15]

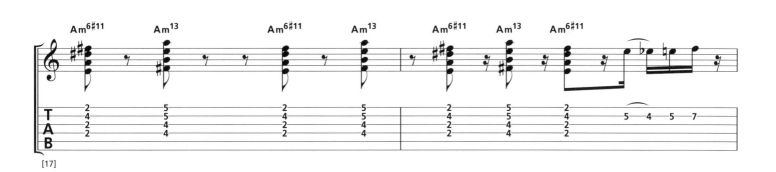

[17]

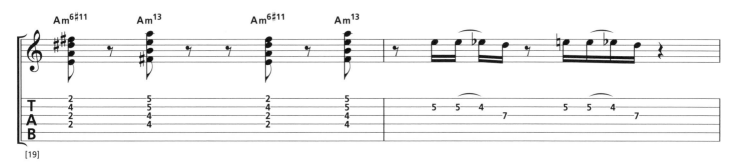

[19]

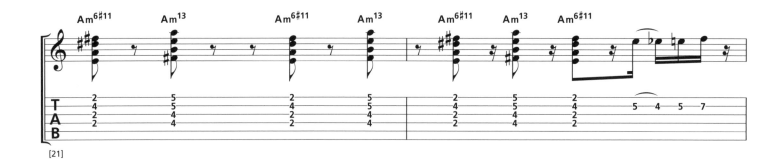

[21]

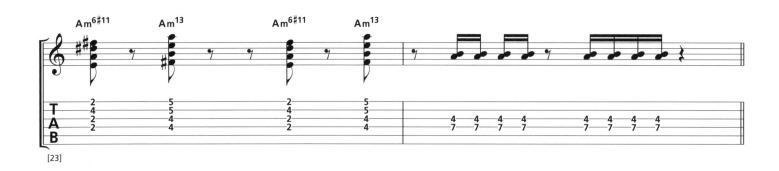

[23]

Bass Solo (16 bars)
Develop on repeat

C

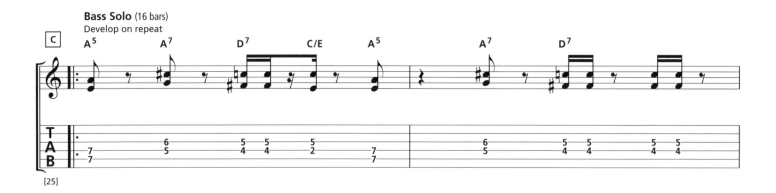

[25]

[27]

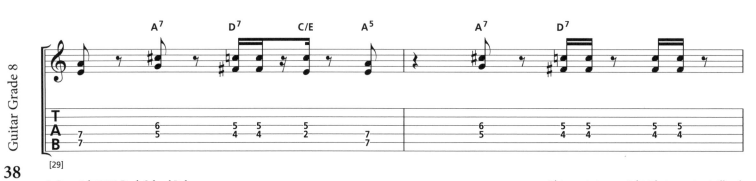

[29]

[31]

D **Drum Solo** (16 bars)
N.C.

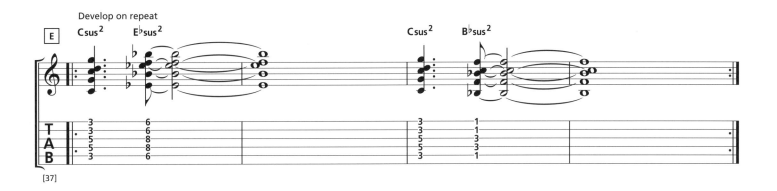

[33]

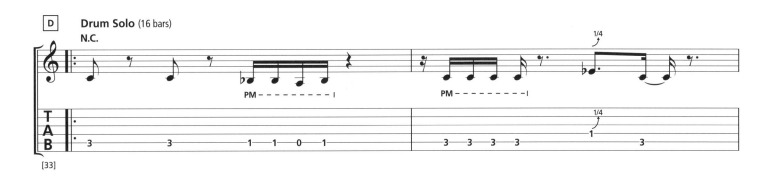

[35]

Develop on repeat

E

[37]

F **Guitar Solo** (16 bars)
Am⁷

D.C. al Fine
Play 4 times

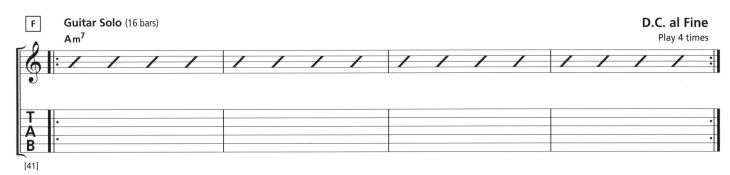

[41]

Walkthrough

Amp Settings

Use a clean tone for all of the sections apart from the solo where you may prefer to use a distorted sound. Aim for an overdriven sound with plenty of middle and a little reverb. A chorus pedal is often used in this style.

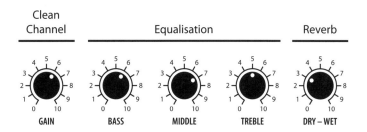

A & G Sections (Bars 1–8)

The A section is a heavily syncopated staccato riff based on an A diminished chord.

Bars 1–44 | *Syncopation*
There are many challenging syncopated parts in 'Dark Matter'. Most have distinctive grooves and should feel fairly natural. However, you may find that some require more in-depth study so break down each beat into 16th notes to see where each note falls.

Bar 4 | *Picking patterns*
While it usually feels natural to start phrases with a down stroke, the first two sequences in bar 4 start on the second and fourth 16th notes of their respective beats. Starting with an upstroke will place the down strokes on the stronger beats and give the phrase a more natural feel (Fig. 1).

B & H Sections (Bars 9–24)

The B section is also heavily syncopated and uses discordant major 7th intervals interspersed with bursts of 16th notes. This part is developed with the inclusion of four-note chords that contain the original major 7th intervals.

Bars 9–15 | *Major 7th intervals*
Make sure that you play the notated major 7th intervals, which can easily be mistaken for octaves (Fig. 2).

C Section (Bars 25–32)

The C section is the bass solo accompanied by the guitar playing funky diads. You have the opportunity to develop this part on the repeat.

Bars 25–32 | *Note lengths*
Correct note lengths are key to the feel of this tight, funky riff. Ensure the notes are allowed to ring on. Listen to the recording and really lock in with the bass and drums.

D & E Sections (Bars 33–40)

The D section is the drum solo accompanied by another single-note riff. The E section is a chordal part that uses suspended chords and, once again, you have the opportunity to develop the part on the repeat.

Bars 37–40 | *Develop on repeat*
When you develop a part be faithful to the original notation while still taking the section somewhere new. Common ways to develop a part are to vary the rhythm or use different chord voicings. These are, of course, only suggestions and you should play the part as you feel works best.

F Section (Bars 41–44)

The F section is a 16-bar guitar solo and is based in A minor. The single chord vamp is an excellent opportunity to explore more adventurous scale choices.

Bars 41–44 | *Guitar solo*
Although the guitar solo is based on a single Am^7 chord, simply using the blues or minor pentatonic scale is unlikely to yield a stylistically convincing result. Fusion guitarists are well-known for their use of exotic scales and arpeggios as well as a large amount of chromaticism. Experiment with different scale choices to increase your options for this solo. The dorian and phrygian modes are a good place to start.

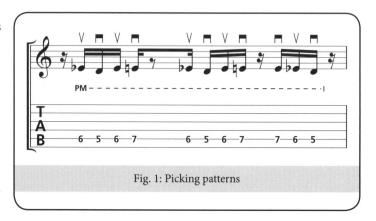

Fig. 1: Picking patterns

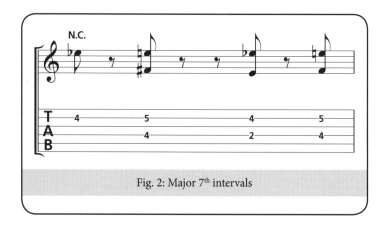

Fig. 2: Major 7th intervals

Technical Exercises

In this section the examiner will ask you to play a selection of exercises drawn from each of the four groups shown below. Groups A, B and C contain examples of the scales and modes, arpeggios and chords you can use when playing the pieces. In Group D you will be asked to prepare *one* stylistic study from the three printed. Your choice of stylistic study will determine the style of the Quick Study Piece.

You do not need to memorise the exercises (and can use the book in the exam) but the examiner will be looking for the speed of your response. The examiner will also give credit for the level of your musicality.

Before you start the section you will be asked whether you would like to play the exercises along with the click or hear a single bar of click before you commence the test. The tempo is ♩ = 100.

Group A: Scales

Two octaves, two positions. The first position is to be prepared on the E string from the starting notes of G–B chromatically. The second position is to be prepared on the A string from the starting notes of C–E chromatically.

1. Whole tone (G whole tone shown, root on E string)

2. Diminished (D diminished shown, root on A string)

3. Altered (C altered shown, root on A string)

Group B: Arpeggios

One octave, two positions. The first position is to be prepared on the E string from the starting notes of G–B chromatically. The second position is to be prepared on the A string from the starting notes of C–E chromatically.

1. Dominant$^{7\sharp5}$ arpeggios (G$^{7\sharp5}$ arpeggio shown, root on E string)

2. Dominant$^{7\flat5}$ arpeggios (A$^{7\flat5}$ arpeggio shown, root on E string)

3. Minor$^{7\flat5}$ arpeggios (Cm$^{7\flat5}$ arpeggio shown, root on A string)

4. Dominant$^{7\sharp9}$ arpeggios (D$^{7\sharp9}$ arpeggio shown, root on A string)

5. Dominant$^{7\flat9}$ arpeggios (E$^{7\flat9}$ arpeggio shown, root on A string)

6. Diminished arpeggios (A diminished arpeggio shown, root on E string)

Group C: Chords

To be prepared in two positions. The first position is to be prepared on the E string from the starting notes of G–B chromatically. The second position is to be prepared on the A string from the starting notes of C–E chromatically. Chords should be strummed and then picked (arpeggiated).

1. Dominant $^{7\sharp5}$ (G $^{7\sharp5}$ chord shown, root on E string)

2. Dominant $^{7\flat5}$ (A $^{7\flat5}$ chord shown, root on E string)

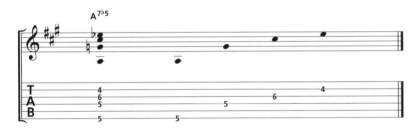

3. Dominant $^{7\sharp9}$ (D $^{7\sharp9}$ arpeggio shown, root on A string)

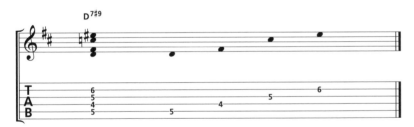

4. Dominant $^{7\flat9}$ (E $^{7\flat9}$ arpeggio shown, root on A string)

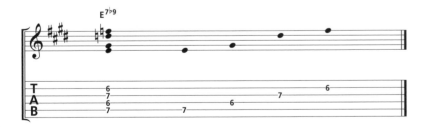

Group D: Stylistic Studies

You will prepare a technical study from one group of styles from the list below. Your choice of style will determine the style of the Quick Study Piece.

1. Rock/Metal: crossing strings and alternate picking

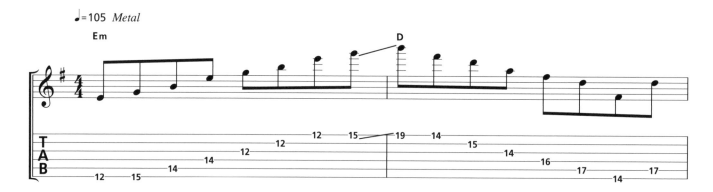

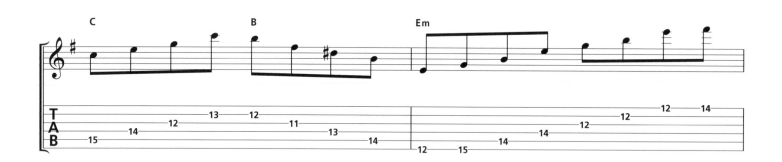

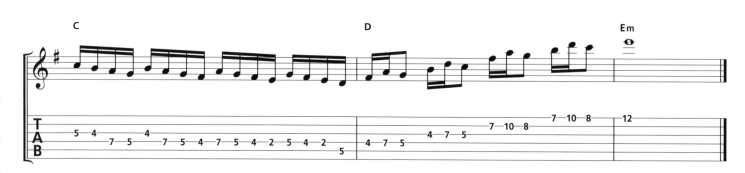

Guitar Grade 8

44

2. Funk: chordal embellishments and muted strings

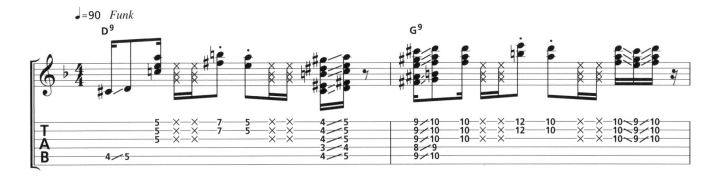

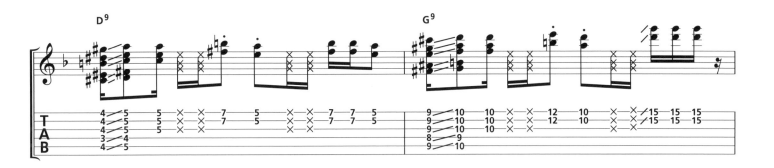

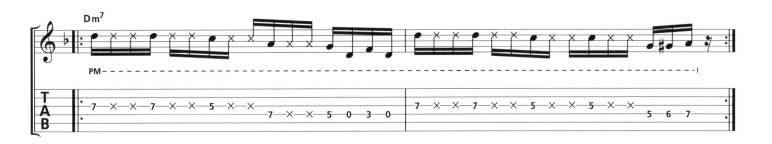

3. Jazz/Latin/Blues: legato phrasing and alternate picking

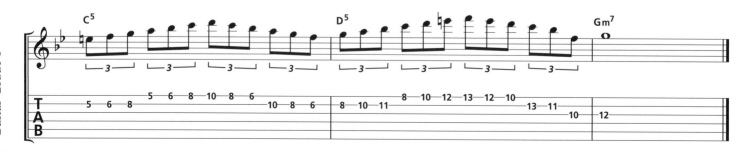

Quick Study Piece

At this grade you will be asked to prepare and play a short Quick Study Piece (QSP). Printed below are three examples of the type of QSP you are likely to receive in the exam. You will be shown the test and played the track with the *notated parts played*. Any bars that require improvisation will not be demonstrated. You will then have three minutes to study the test. The backing track will be played twice more. You will be allowed to practise during the first playing of the backing track, with the notated parts now absent, before playing it to the examiner on the second playing of the backing track.

The style of your QSP is determined by the stylistic study you selected in the technical exercise section. The QSP is in the form of a lead sheet and it is up to you to create your own interpretation of the music in the parts marked for improvisation.

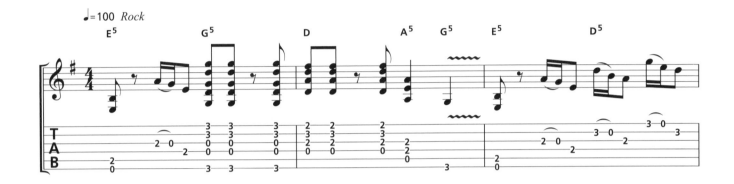

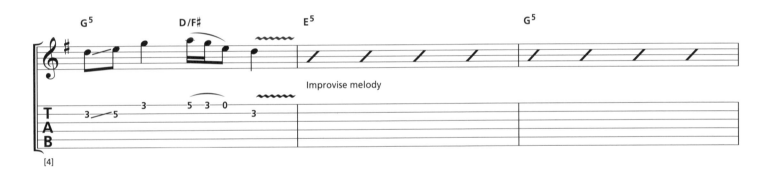

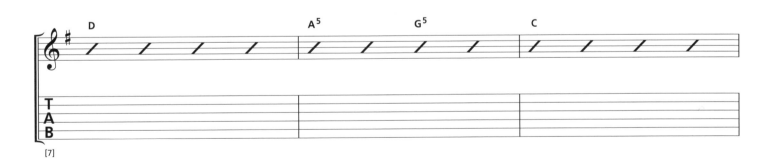

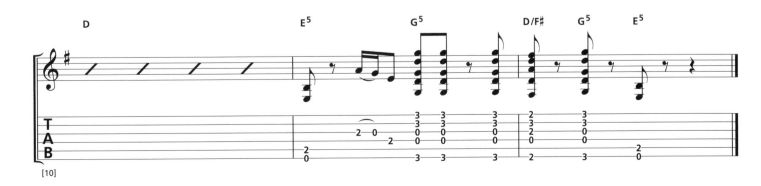

Quick Study Piece

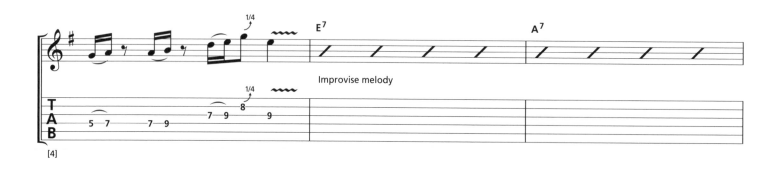

Improvise melody

[4]

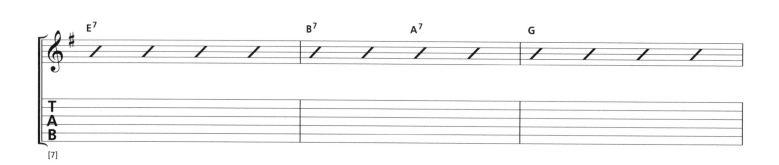

[7]

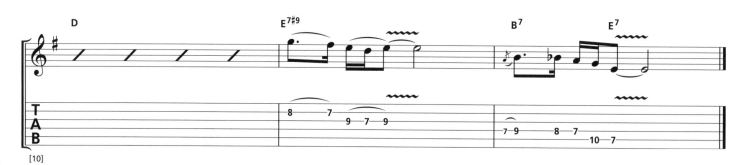

[10]

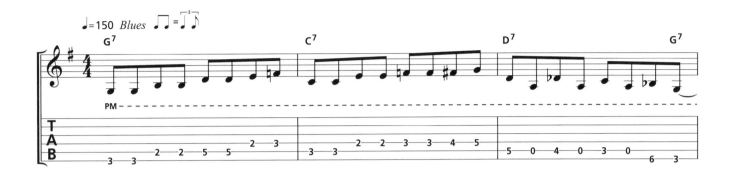

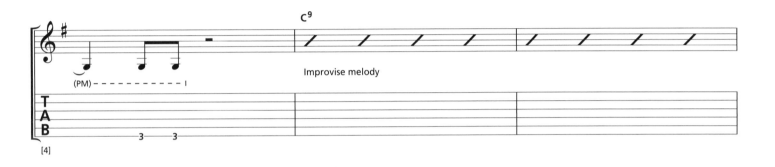

[4]

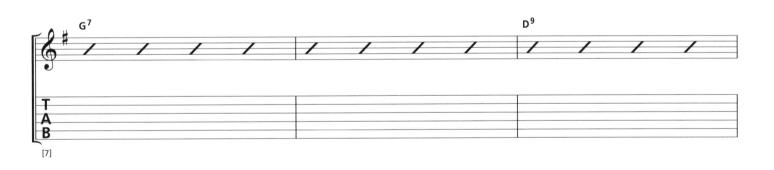

[7]

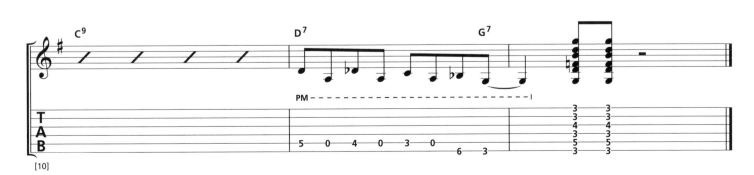

[10]

Ear Tests

There are two ear tests in this grade. The examiner will play each test to you twice. You will find one example of each type of test printed below.

Test 1: Melodic Recall

The examiner will play you a two bar melody with a bass and drum backing using either the E major pentatonic, F minor pentatonic or B natural minor scales. The first note of the melody will be *either* the root note, third *or* fifth and the first interval will be *either* ascending *or* descending. You will play the melody back on your instrument. You will hear the test twice.

Each time the test is played the sequence is: count-in, root note, count-in, melody. There will be a short gap for you to practise after you have heard the test for the second time. You will hear the count-in and root note for the third time followed by a *vocal* count-in and you will then play the melody to the bass and drum backing. The tempo is ♩=90.

Test 2: Harmonic Recall

The examiner will play you a tonic chord followed by a four bar chord sequence in the key of E major played to a bass and drum backing. The sequence will use the I, ii, iii, IV, V and vi chords. The I and IV chords can be either major or major[7] chords. You will be asked to play the chord sequence to the bass and drum backing in the rhythm show in the example below. This rhythm will be used in all examples of this test given in the exam. You will then be asked to identify the sequence you have played to the examiner, including any chord extensions. You will hear the test twice.

Each time the test is played the sequence is: count-in, tonic, count-in, chords. There will be a short gap for you to practise after you have heard the test for the second time. You will hear the count-in and tonic for the third time followed by a *vocal* count-in and you will then play the chords to the bass and drum backing. You should then name the chords, including any extensions. The tempo is ♩=90.

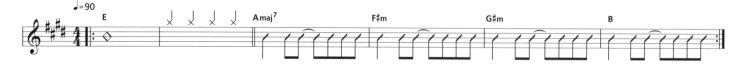

General Musicianship Questions

In this part of the exam you will be asked five questions. Four of these questions will be about general music knowledge and the fifth question will be asked about your instrument.

Music Knowledge

The examiner will ask you four music knowledge questions based on a piece of music that you have played in the exam. You will nominate the piece of music about which the questions will be asked. In this grade you will be asked to identify and demonstrate your answers on your instrument as directed by the examiner. The scale question at the end of the list of subjects is mandatory.

In Grade 8 you will be asked to explain:

- The names of pitches

- Any expressive musical marking found in the piece such as palm muting, accents, staccato, legato, vibrato, natural and artificial harmonics

- Any dynamic marking found in the piece

- The types of scale that can be used appropriately in the solo section of the piece you have played and its relation to the underlying harmony of the piece

Instrument Knowledge

The examiner will also ask you one question regarding your instrument.

In Grade 8 you will be asked to explain and demonstrate:

- Where to find the same pitch on two different strings

- The function of the volume and tone controls on your guitar

- The set up for the tone required for the piece you have played on the amp

- How to achieve changes in tone in a song

Further Information

Tips on how to approach this part of this exam can be found in the *Syllabus Guide* for guitar, the Rockschool *Guitar Companion Guide* and on the Rockschool website: *www.rockschool.co.uk*. The Introduction to Tone, a comprehensive explanation of guitar tones, can be found at the back of each grade book and the tone guide to each piece is in the appropriate Walkthrough.

Entering Rockschool Exams

Entering a Rockschool exam is easy. You may enter either online at *www.rockschool.co.uk* or by downloading and filling in an exam entry form. Information on current exam fees can be obtained from Rockschool online or by calling +44 (0)845 460 4747.

- You should enter for your exam when you feel ready.

- You may enter for any one of the three examination periods shown below with their closing dates:

EXAMINATION PERIODS

PERIOD	DURATION	CLOSING DATE
Period A	1st February to 31st March	1st December
Period B	1st May to 31st July	1st April
Period C	23rd October to 15th December	1st October

These dates apply from 1st September 2012 until further notice

- The full Rockschool examination terms and conditions can be downloaded from our website. The information shown below is a summary.

- Please complete your entry with the information required. Fill in the type and level of exam and instrument, along with the examination period and year. Paper entry forms should be sent with a cheque or postal order (payable to Rockschool Ltd) to the address shown on the entry form. Entry forms sent by post will be acknowledged either by letter or email, while all entries made online will automatically be acknowledged by email.

- Applications received after the expiry of the closing date, whether made by post or online, may be accepted subject to the payment of a late fee.

- Rockschool will allocate your exam to a specific centre and you will receive notification of the exam showing a date, location and time, as well as advice on what to bring to the centre. We endeavour to give you four weeks notice ahead of your exam date.

- You should inform Rockschool of any cancellations or alterations to the schedule as soon as you can because it may not be possible to transfer entries from one centre, or one period, to another without the payment of an additional fee.

- Please bring your music book and CD to the exam. You may use photocopied music if this helps you avoid awkward page turns. The examiner will sign each book during each examination. Please note, you may be barred from taking an exam if you use someone else's music.

- You should aim to arrive for your exam 15 minutes before the time stated on the schedule. Guitarists and bass players should get ready to enter the exam room by taking their instrument from its case and tuning up. This will help with the smooth running of each exam day.

- Each Grade 8 exam is scheduled to last 30 minutes. You can use a small proportion of this time to set up and check the sound levels.

- You will receive a copy of the examiner's marksheet two to three weeks after the exam. If you have passed you will also receive a Rockschool certificate of achievement.

Guitar Grade 8 Marking Schemes

ELEMENT	PASS	MERIT	DISTINCTION
Performance Piece 1	12–14 out of 20	15–17 out of 20	18+ out of 20
Performance Piece 2	12–14 out of 20	15–17 out of 20	18+ out of 20
Performance Piece 3	12–14 out of 20	15–17 out of 20	18+ out of 20
Technical Exercises	9–10 out of 15	11–12 out of 15	13+ out of 15
Quick Study Piece	6 out of 10	7–8 out of 10	9+ out of 10
Ear Tests	6 out of 10	7–8 out of 10	9+ out of 10
General Musicianship Questions	3 out of 5	4 out of 5	5 out of 5
TOTAL MARKS	60%+	74%+	90%+

PERFORMANCE CERTIFICATES | GRADES 1–8

ELEMENT	PASS	MERIT	DISTINCTION
Performance Piece 1	12–14 out of 20	15–17 out of 20	18+ out of 20
Performance Piece 2	12–14 out of 20	15–17 out of 20	18+ out of 20
Performance Piece 3	12–14 out of 20	15–17 out of 20	18+ out of 20
Performance Piece 4	12–14 out of 20	15–17 out of 20	18+ out of 20
Performance Piece 5	12–14 out of 20	15–17 out of 20	18+ out of 20
TOTAL MARKS	60%+	75%+	90%+

Introduction to Tone

A large part of an effective guitar performance is selecting the right tone. The electric guitar's sound is subject to a wide range of variables, and this guide outlines the basic controls present on most amplifiers as well as the common variations between models. There is also a basic overview of pickups and the effect their location on the guitar has on tone. Finally, it covers the differences between the types of distortion, which is crucial to getting your basic sound right.

At Grade 8 the tone may change within the course of a piece. You should aim to use a tone that is stylistically appropriate and you may bring your own equipment to the exam room for this purpose. There is a tone guide at the start of each walkthrough to help you.

Basic amplifier controls

Most amplifiers come with a standard set of controls that are the same as, or very similar to, the diagram below. It's important to understand what each control is and the effect that it has on your guitar's tone.

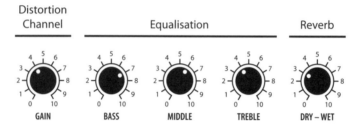

- **Channel (Clean/Distortion)**

  Most amplifiers have two channels that can be selected either by a switch on the amp or a footswitch. One channel is usually 'clean' while the other can be driven harder to create a distorted (or 'dirty') tone. If your amp doesn't have two channels, look at the 'variation of basic controls' below to see how to get clean and dirty tones from a one channel amp.

- **Gain**

  In simple terms, the gain determines how hard you drive the amp. This governs how distorted the dirty (also called 'drive', 'overdrive', or 'distortion') channel is and acts as a second volume control on the clean channel (though a high gain setting will distort even the clean channel).

- **Bass**

  This adjusts the lowest frequencies. Boost it to add warmth and reduce or 'cut' it if your sound is muddy or woolly.

- **Middle**

  This is the most important equalisation (often shortened to just 'EQ') control. Most of the guitar's tonal character is found in the mid-range so adjusting this control has a lot of impact upon your tone. Boosting it with a dirty sound will create a more classic rock tone while cutting it will produce a more metal one.

- **Treble**

  This adjusts the high frequencies. Boost it to add brightness and cut it if the sound is too harsh or brittle.

- **Reverb**

  Short for 'reverberation'. This artificially recreates the ambience of your guitar in a large room, usually a hall. This dial controls the balance between the 'dry' (the sound without the reverb) and 'wet' (the sound with the reverb) sounds.

Variations of basic controls

The diagram above shows the most common amp controls. There are many variations to this basic setup, which can often be confusing. The following section is a breakdown of some of the other amp controls you may encounter:

- **Presence control**

  Sometimes this dial replaces the 'middle' control and other times it appears in addition to it. It adjusts the higher mid-range frequencies (those found between the 'middle' and 'treble' dials).

- **No reverb control**
Reverb can be a nice addition to your guitar tone but it's not essential. Don't be concerned if your amp doesn't have a reverb control.

- **Volume, gain, master setup**
Single channel amplifiers often have an extra volume control (in addition to the master volume) located next to the gain control. For clean sounds, keep the gain set low and the volume similarly low and use the master control for overall volume. If the master control is on 10 and you require more level, turn the volume control up. However, you may find that this starts to distort as you reach the higher numbers.

To get a distorted tone, turn the volume down low and the gain up until you get the amount of distortion you require. Regulate the overall level with master volume. If the master control is on 10 and you require more level simply turn the volume up. In this case, however, you may find you lose clarity before you reach maximum.

Pickups

Entire books have been devoted to the intricacies of pickups. However, three basic pieces of information will help you understand a lot about your guitar tone:

- **Singlecoils**
These narrow pickups are fitted to many guitars. The Fender Stratocaster is the most famous guitar fitted with singlecoils. They produce a bright, cutting sound that can sound a little thin in some situations, especially heavier styles of rock music.

- **Humbuckers**
This type of pickup was originally designed to remove or 'buck' the hum produced by singlecoil pickups, hence the name. They produce a warm, mellow sound compared to singlecoil pickups but have a tendency to sound a little muddy in some situations. They are usually identifiable because they are twice the width of a singlecoil pickup. The Gibson Les Paul is a well-known guitar fitted with humbucking pickups.

- **Pickup location**
Basically, pickups located near the guitar's neck will have the warmest sound and those located near the bridge will have the brightest sound.

Different types of 'dirty' tones

There are lots of different words to describe the 'dirty' guitar sounds. In fact, all the sounds are 'distortions' of the clean tone, which can be confusing when you consider there's a 'type' of distortion called 'distortion'. Below is a simplified breakdown of the three main types of dirty sounds, plus some listening material to help you through this tonal minefield:

- **Overdrive**
This is the 'mildest' form of distortion. It can be quite subtle and only evident when the guitar is played strongly. It can be also be full-on and aggressive.
Hear it on: Cream – 'Sunshine Of Your Love', AC/DC – 'Back In Black', Oasis – 'Cigarettes and Alcohol'.

- **Distortion**
This is usually associated with heavier styles of music. It's dense and the most extreme of the dirty tones and is usually associated with heavy styles of music.
Hear it on: Metallica – 'Enter Sandman', Avenged Sevenfold – 'Bat Country', Bon Jovi – 'You Give Love A Bad Name'.

- **Fuzz**
As the name implies, fuzz is a broken, 'fuzzy' sound. It was popular in the 1960s but, while still evident in certain genres, it's less common now.
Hear it on: Jimi Hendrix Experience – 'Purple Haze', The Kinks – 'You Really Got Me'.

Guitar Notation Explained

THE MUSICAL STAVE shows pitches and rhythms and is divided by lines into bars. Pitches are named after the first seven letters of the alphabet.

TABLATURE graphically represents the guitar fingerboard. Each horizontal line represents a string and each number represents a fret.

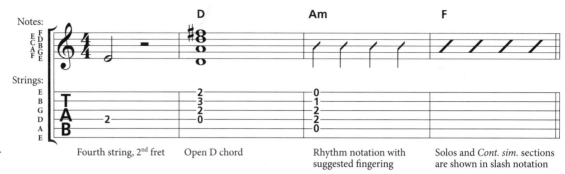

Fourth string, 2nd fret — Open D chord — Rhythm notation with suggested fingering — Solos and *Cont. sim.* sections are shown in slash notation

Definitions For Special Guitar Notation

HAMMER-ON: Pick the lower note, then sound the higher note by fretting it without picking.

PULL-OFF: Pick the higher note then sound the lower note by lifting the finger without picking.

SLIDE: Pick the first note and slide to the next. If the line connects (as below) the second note is *not* repicked.

GLISSANDO: Slide off of a note at the end of its rhythmic value. The note that follows *is* repicked.

STRING BENDS: Pick the first note then bend (or release the bend) to the pitch indicated in brackets.

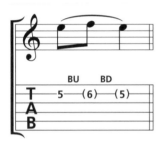

VIBRATO: Vibrate the note by bending and releasing the string smoothly and continuously.

TRILL: Rapidly alternate between the two bracketed notes by hammering on and pulling off.

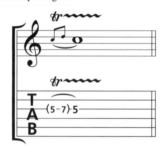

NATURAL HARMONICS: Lightly touch the string above the indicated fret then pick to sound a harmonic.

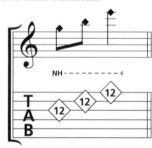

PINCHED HARMONICS: Bring the thumb of the picking hand into contact with the string immediately after the pick.

PICK-HAND TAP: Strike the indicated note with a finger from the picking hand. Usually followed by a pull-off.

FRET-HAND TAP: As pick-hand tap, but use fretting hand. Usually followed by a pull-off or hammer-on.

QUARTER-TONE BEND: Pick the note indicated and bend the string up by a quarter tone.

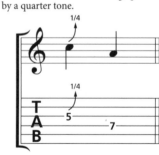

PRE-BENDS: Before picking the note, bend the string from the fret indicated between the staves, to the equivalent pitch indicated in brackets in the TAB.

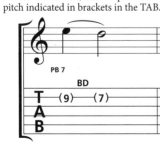

WHAMMY BAR BEND: Use the whammy bar to bend notes to the pitches indicated in brackets in the TAB.

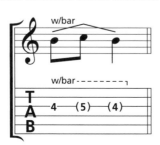

D.%. al Coda

D.C. al Fine

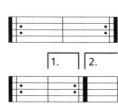

- Go back to the sign (%), then play until the bar marked **To Coda** ⊕ then skip to the section marked ⊕ **Coda**.

- Go back to the beginning of the song and play until the bar marked **Fine** (end).

- Repeat the bars between the repeat signs.

- When a repeated section has different endings, play the first ending only the first time and the second ending only the second time.